and the Children

by Erin Furyk
illustrated by Laure Fournier

SCHOOL PUBLISHERS

Printed in China

ISBN 10: 0-15-350493-5
ISBN 13: 978-0-15-350493-8

Ordering Options
ISBN 10: 0-15-350333-5 (Grade 3 Below-Level Collection)
ISBN 13: 978-0-15-350333-7 (Grade 3 Below-Level Collection)
ISBN 10: 0-15-357479-8 (package of 5)
ISBN 13: 978-0-15-357479-5 (package of 5)

2 3 4 5 6 7 8 9 10 985 12 11 10 09 08 07

"I caught another one!" cried Luana. She tossed the silver fish into the bottom of the boat, along with the others. "We have enough fish," she said. "Let's go home now."

"No," said Kekoa. "It's a nice day. Let's row out farther where there are bigger fish."

"Mother says not to go out too far," said Luana.

"She'll be delighted if we catch a big fish, though," said Kekoa.

Luana didn't argue. It was a beautiful day. Behind them was the Big Island, Hawaii. The time is long ago. Tall green trees reached for the sky. Bright flowers added dots of color.

Before them was the ocean. The water sparkled in the sunlight.

Someone else was enjoying the day, too. Beneath the water, Mano the shark watched them.

"Look at these lovely children," he thought. "I must get to them somehow." He swam toward them.

"Children," Mano called in a voice disguised to sound like a man. "It's Uncle Mano. Please come with me."

"We don't have an uncle named Mano," said Kekoa.

"Yes, you do," said Mano. "I've just been away a long time."

"Where do you want to take us?" asked Luana.

"I know where there are beautiful pearls," said the cunning Mano. "We can make a lovely gift for your mother."

Luana and Kekoa looked at each other. Mother loved pearls. The gift would make her happy.

"All right," said Kekoa. "Please show us."

Mano stuck one of his fins into the side of the boat to pull it. Then he swam, using his other fin and tail.

He pulled the boat far into the ocean.
Luana began to get nervous.

"We're going very far," said Luana.
"I'm going to tell him to stop."

She leaned over the side of the boat.
Suddenly, she saw Mano's sharp white
teeth. Mano was a shark!

Luana whispered the horrible truth to Kekoa. They had to do something fast.

"Uncle Mano," said Kekoa. "You are working very hard. Would you like a fish?" The idea of a fresh, tender fish made Mano pause.

"Here," said Luana. She tossed a fish into the water behind them.

Mano eagerly swam back toward the fish. He caught it and ate it, snapping its brittle bones.

"Now I'll get back to business," he thought.

He was about to turn back. Then Luana tossed another fish into the water. Mano couldn't resist.
He ate that fish, too.

The children kept tossing fish into the water. Mano kept following them. Soon they were close to shore. They only had one fish left.

"Here is our best fish," said Luana, tossing it onto the sand.

Mano chased after it. Then he realized his mistake.

"Children, get me back into the water!" he cried.

It was too late, though. Luana and Kekoa had beached their boat and raced away. They ran home to Mother. They told her the terrible tale.

"Now we don't have any fish, though," said Luana.

"That's all right," said Mother as she embraced them. "I know where we can find a nice shark."

"No!" laughed Luana and Kekoa.

Think Critically

1. How is this story like *Lon Po Po*? How is it different?

2. Why does Kekoa want to row out farther?

3. What does the shark say to the children in order to trick them?

4. What do you learn about Mano when he decides to chase after the fish?

5. Would you want to live where Kekoa and Luana live? Why or why not?

 Language Arts

Write a Journal Pretend that you are one of the children. Write a journal entry describing what happened with the shark and how you felt when it was over.

School-Home Connection Share this story with a family member. Then act it out together. Use different voices for different characters.